Two Days in Summer

STUDENTS' WORKBOOK

8 193

Brian Abbs/Ingrid Freebairn
Video script by Jim Hill

Longman

CAST OF PLAYERS

Eddy	Jonathan Caplan
Security guard	James Taylor
Mr Archer	David Beale
Annie	Moira Brooker
Maribel	Yolanda Vasquez
Lisa	Susan Beagley
John	Peter Doran
Mr Judd	Michael Garner
Mr Potter	Roger Booth
Skater	Paul McKenzie
Museum attendant 1	Ruddy L Davis
Museum attendant 2	John Owens
Shop assistant 1	Kim Clifford
Shop assistant 2	Maggie Guess

Video script by Jim Hill

Production by London Weekend Television

Directed by Nigel Miller

Acknowledgements
We are grateful to the following for permission to reproduce
copyright photographs:

Associated Press Ltd for page 19 bottom right; Longman
Photographic Unit for page 19 bottom left; Picturepoint Ltd for
page 8 top right, page 19 top right, page 44 top right and page 51
top right; The Victoria and Albert Museum for page 24 top right.

We are grateful to Roger Morton for all other photographs used in
the book.

We are indebted to Independent Television Publications Ltd and
Solo Syndication & Literary Agency Ltd for permission to use the
ITV London TV Guide from p. 32 *Daily Mail* 9/10/86 ©
Independent Television Publications Ltd 1986.

Longman Group UK Limited
Longman House, Burnt Mill, Harlow,
Essex CM20 2JE, England
and Associated Companies throughout the world.

© Longman Group UK Limited 1987

First published 1987
ISBN 0-582-91765-4

Set in Gill Sans light
Printed in Great Britain
by Scotprint, Musselburgh

CONTENTS

| UNIT 1 | 00.01 | 4 |

Greet people formally and informally
through the day
Ask for and say your name, address
and telephone number
Thank people informally

| UNIT 2 | 04.30 | 8 |

Greet people formally and informally
Ask for help
Introduce yourself and others
Give your nationality and say where
you are from
Talk about possession
Ask and talk about present activities
Say what you are wearing

| UNIT 3 | 07.22 | 12 |

Greet friends informally
Talk about likes and dislikes
Say where you and others live
Ask and talk about jobs and
occupations
Express ambition
Spell your name and address
Say goodbye

| UNIT 4 | 11.00 | 16 |

Ask what people want
Talk about likes and dislikes
Talk about age
Ask and talk about money
Apologise and accept apologies

| UNIT 5 | 13.23 | 20 |

Consolidation

| UNIT 6 | 16.12 | 24 |

Ask and talk about past events
Ask for and give directions
Ask and say where you buy things
Ask and talk about times

| UNIT 7 | 20.19 | 28 |

Ask and talk about present activities
Ask and talk about routines and habits
Talk about personal details
Ask and talk about present states

| UNIT 8 | 22.34 | 32 |

Talk about journeys
Offer food, drink and hospitality
Accept and refuse offers with
explanations
Talk about the home
Make decisions

| UNIT 9 | 27.40 | 36 |

Talk on the telephone
Ask and talk about plans
Invite people to do things
Accept invitations
Ask for and make suggestions
Give an opinion with a reason

| UNIT 10 | 30.47 | 40 |

Consolidation

| UNIT 11 | 34.19 | 44 |

Express appreciation
Ask and talk about size and price
Ask and talk about buying and paying

| UNIT 12 | 40.18 | 48 |

Give orders
Confirm things
Ask about past activities
Narrate past events in sequence
Invite formally
Refuse invitations politely and firmly

| UNIT 13 | 42.36 | 52 |

Interrogate
Ask for confirmation
Talk about continuing events

| UNIT 14 | 45.19 | 56 |

Talk about possession
Identify places
Ask and talk about completed actions
Make promises
Report requests
Thank formally

| UNIT 15 | 47.47 | 60 |

Consolidation

BACKGROUND

Waterloo Station is one of London's main line railway stations. Trains from Waterloo go to the south and south-west of England.

LANGUAGE USE

Greet people formally through the day	Good morning/afternoon.
Greet people informally	Hi!
Ask for names	What's your name?
	What was your name?
	Who are you?
Say your name	I'm Eddy./It's Eddy.
Say your address	It's 12 Liston Road, Woking.
Say your telephone number	It's 722 1907.
Thank people informally	Thanks.

WORDS AND EXPRESSIONS

address	confidential	Good afternoon.
airport	late	Good morning.
bag		Have a good time.
book	call	I'm in a hurry.
computer	can	Just a minute.
filing	collect	Sorry I'm late.
film	have	Thanks.
floor	have got	Thanks. And you.
holiday	have to	
keys	make	
name	sign	
phone number	stay	
road		
sister	How long?	
security	What?	
video camera	Where?	
weekend	Who?	
	Why?	

VIEW AND ANSWER

I. Answer the questions.

1. How does Eddy travel to London?

   (He travels) By train.

2. What time does he arrive?

   ....

3. What is he carrying?

   ....
   ....

4. What has he got in his hand?

   ....
   ....

5. Where is he going?

   ....

6. Where does the girl put the keys of the filing cabinet?

   ....

CHECK

2. Number the pictures in the correct order.

d)

> I've come to see my sister … She's expecting me. I'm collecting some keys.

a)

> The door keys are on the desk. How long are you staying?

Number ....

Number ....

> Oi! Just a minute … You have to sign this book.

c)

Number ....

b)

> Security!

Number ....

> I'm going to Four, are you?

> Me too.

e)

Number ....

3. Look at the pictures and write the correct name under each person.

| Mr Archer | Eddy Taylor | the security guard | Annie Taylor |

1. Eddy Taylor   2. ....   3. ....   4. ....

4. Circle the right answer.

1. Annie is Eddy's   (a) sister.
                       b) girlfriend.

2. On the telephone   a) Eddy.
   the security guard   b) Freddy.
   calls Eddy   c) Teddy.

3. Eddy is carrying   a) a computer.
                        b) a video camera.

4. Eddy wants   a) to collect some keys.
                       b) to see Mr Archer.

5. Annie is going   a) on holiday.
                       b) home.

6. Eddy takes the keys a) of his sister's flat.
                        b) of the filing cabinet.

DESCRIBE

Describe Eddy and Mr Archer. Say how old they are and what they look like.

VIEW AND LISTEN FOR DETAIL

5. Who said the following? Tick the correct person.

1. `02.13` The bag and the camera, please.

   Eddy   Annie   security guard ✓

2. `03.12` What about your holiday?

   Eddy   Mr Archer   Annie

3. `03.16` Hi, sis. Sorry I'm late.

   Annie   Eddy   Mr Archer

4. `03.20` The door keys are on the desk.

   Mr Archer   Eddy   Annie

---

6. Complete the conversation.

`01.18`

Eddy: Morning.

Security guard: It's afternoon.

Eddy: ...Good afternoon...........

Security guard: And who are you?

Eddy: .... Taylor.

                 I've come to see ....

                 ....

Security guard: Oh, er ... Miss Taylor? I have Freddy Taylor here for you.

Eddy: ...., not ....

ROLEPLAY

Roleplay a similar conversation.

1. It is 9.30 in the morning. You want to see Mr Archer. Your name is Ann Brown. The security guard in Reception thinks your name is Jan Brown.

2. It is 2.30 in the afternoon. You want to see Mrs Jones. Your name is Ted Roberts. The receptionist thinks your name is Fred Roberts.

Receptionist: Good ...

You: ...

Receptionist: What's your name?

WORD STUDY

7. Label the things in Annie's handbag with the words from the box.

address book	keys	pen	stamps
camera	letter	pencil	ticket
diary	passport	purse	

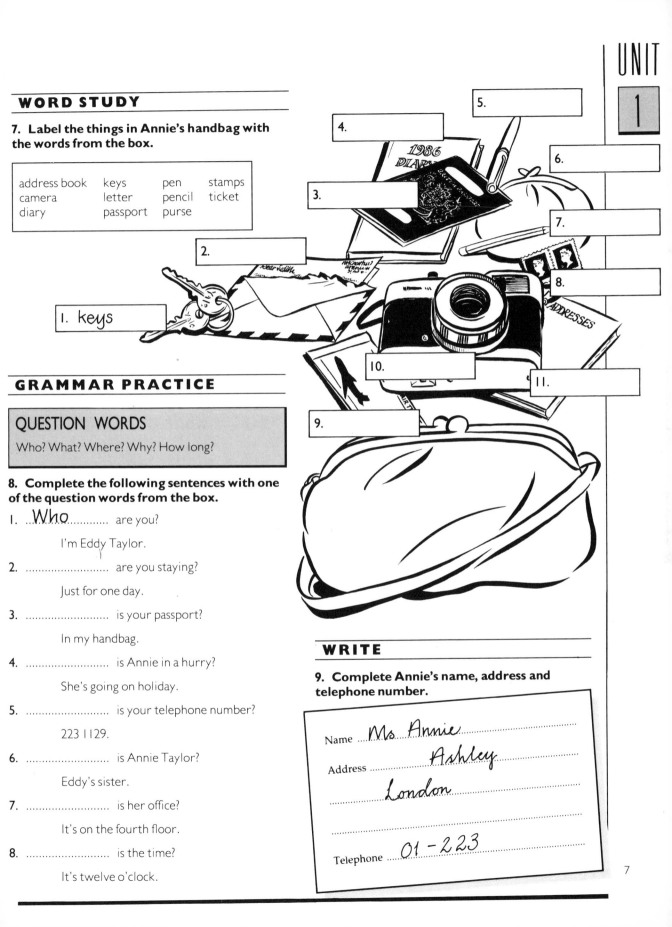

5.

4.

6.

3.

7.

2.

8.

1. keys

10.

11.

9.

GRAMMAR PRACTICE

QUESTION WORDS

Who? What? Where? Why? How long?

8. Complete the following sentences with one of the question words from the box.

1. ...Who........... are you?

   I'm Eddy Taylor.

2. .... are you staying?

   Just for one day.

3. .... is your passport?

   In my handbag.

4. .... is Annie in a hurry?

   She's going on holiday.

5. .... is your telephone number?

   223 1129.

6. .... is Annie Taylor?

   Eddy's sister.

7. .... is her office?

   It's on the fourth floor.

8. .... is the time?

   It's twelve o'clock.

WRITE

9. Complete Annie's name, address and telephone number.

Name ...Ms Annie.......................

Address ....Ashley................

..............London.................................

....

Telephone ....01 – 223....................

7

UNIT
2
04.30

BACKGROUND

For many hundreds of years Covent Garden was London's main fruit and vegetable market. Now it is a lively shopping centre with many small boutiques and market stalls. There are also many pubs, cafes, wine bars and restaurants. Because Covent Garden is near the theatre district, it is a popular place for both visitors and Londoners.

LANGUAGE USE

Greet people informally	Hello.
Greet people formally	How do you do?
	Pleased to meet you.
Ask for help	Can you help me?
Introduce yourself	I'm Maribel.
	I'm a student.
Introduce others	This is Miss (Annie) Taylor.
Give your nationality	I'm Spanish.
Say where you are from	I'm from Barcelona.
Talk about possession	He's got my door keys.
Ask and talk about present activities	What are you doing?
	I'm making a film about clothes.
	He's staying at my flat.
Say what you are wearing	I'm wearing a T-shirt.

WORDS AND EXPRESSIONS

blouse	do/does	Can you help me?
brother	find	How do you do?
clothes	follow	I don't know.
college	see (= check)	I don't understand.
fashion	take	I must go now.
friend	think	Pleased to meet you.
jacket	wear	See you around.
jeans		Well done.
leather	black	What about ...?
mistake	easy	
plimsolls	old	
project	orange	
shoes	polka dot	
skirt	white	
street		
student	perhaps	
T-shirt		

VIEW AND ANSWER

1. Answer Yes or No.

Eddy

1. is shopping. ..No....

2. is wearing a new jeans jacket. ....

3. is using a video camera. ....

Maribel

4. is a good friend of Eddy's. ....

5. has blonde hair. ....

6. is wearing a black jacket. ....

Annie

7. is at the airport. ....

8. is with Mr Archer. ....

9. looks angry and upset. ....

10. goes to the airport with the two men. ....

CHECK

2. Look at the pictures and circle the correct statements

1. **a)** Eddy is in Covent Garden.

   b) Eddy is at Waterloo Station.

2. **a)** Eddy meets a girl in the street.

   b) Eddy meets his sister in the street.

3. **a)** She is wearing jeans and a jacket.

   b) She is wearing a skirt and jacket.

4. **a)** Annie and Mr Archer are working together.

   b) Annie is answering Mr Archer's questions.

3. Look at the pictures and write the correct name under each person.

| Mr Judd   Mr Potter   Maribel   Mr Archer   Eddy |

I'm making a film about clothes. Street fashion. It's a college project.

Pleased to meet you.

How do you do?

I must go now, Eddy. That is my friend, Lisa.

Now Miss Taylor, the keys. Where are the keys?

1. Eddy ....

2. ....

3. ....

4. ....

5. ....

4. Answer the questions.

1. Where is Eddy from?

(He's from) Southampton.

2. Is he a film director?

....

3. What is the name of the girl?

....

4. Where is she from?

....

5. Where is Eddy's sister, Annie?

....

6. Who is questioning her? Why?

....

....

7. Who must follow Eddy? Why?

....

....

EXPLAIN

– why Mr Archer says: 'See what he does with the keys.'
– what will happen when Eddy goes to Annie's flat.

VIEW AND LISTEN FOR DETAIL

`05.56`

5. Complete the information about Maribel.

Name: ....

....

Nationality: ....

Home town:

Barcelona

Clothes: ....

....

....

....

....

....

....

....

6. Complete the conversations.

`05.33`

1. Eddy: Hello, I'm .... Eddy .... from
Southampton. .... a ....
and........................... Levi 50ls, a
......................, plimsolls and ....
leather .... See,.......................
Now you.

Maribel: Hello. .... Maribel ....
Barcelona. I am ....
.... friend.

`06.39`

2. Archer: .... Mr Judd and Mr Potter
from security. Gentlemen, ...
....
from computer filing.

Judd: ....

Potter: ....

WORD STUDY

7. Label the clothes and accessories with the words from the box.

bag	jeans	skirt
blouse	shirt	sweater
jacket	shoes	T-shirt

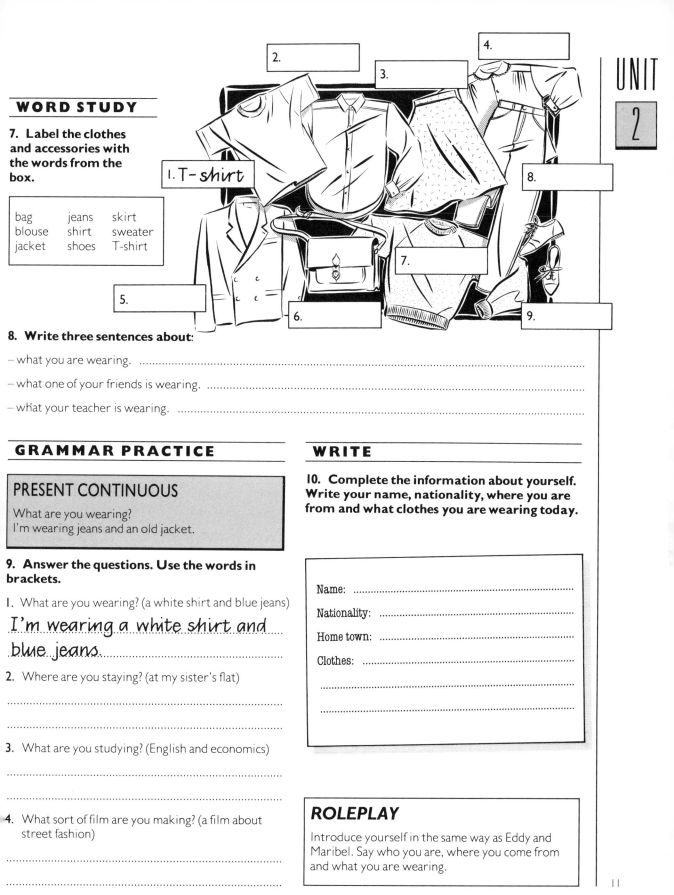

1. T-shirt
2.
3.
4.
5.
6.
7.
8.
9.

8. Write three sentences about:

– what you are wearing. ....

– what one of your friends is wearing. ....

– what your teacher is wearing. ....

GRAMMAR PRACTICE

PRESENT CONTINUOUS

What are you wearing?
I'm wearing jeans and an old jacket.

9. Answer the questions. Use the words in brackets.

1. What are you wearing? (a white shirt and blue jeans)

I'm wearing a white shirt and blue jeans.

2. Where are you staying? (at my sister's flat)

....

....

3. What are you studying? (English and economics)

....

....

4. What sort of film are you making? (a film about street fashion)

....

....

WRITE

10. Complete the information about yourself. Write your name, nationality, where you are from and what clothes you are wearing today.

Name: ....

Nationality: ....

Home town: ....

Clothes: ....

....

....

ROLEPLAY

Introduce yourself in the same way as Eddy and Maribel. Say who you are, where you come from and what you are wearing.

BACKGROUND

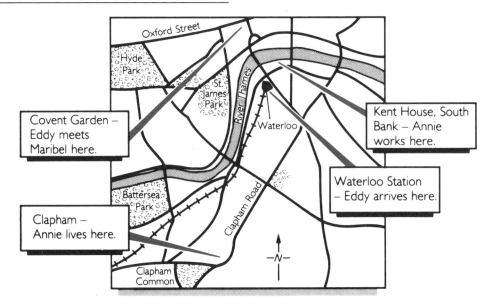

Oxford Street

Hyde Park

St. James Park

River Thames

Waterloo

Covent Garden – Eddy meets Maribel here.

Kent House, South Bank – Annie works here.

Waterloo Station – Eddy arrives here.

Clapham Road

Battersea Park

Clapham – Annie lives here.

—N—

Clapham Common

LANGUAGE USE

Greet friends informally	Hi! How are you?
	Fine, thank you.
Talk about likes and dislikes	I like/don't like fizzy drinks.
Say where you and others live	I'm staying at my sister's house.
	It's in Clapham.
	We live in Clapham too.
Ask and talk about jobs and occupations	I'm a telex operator.
	I'm a part-time student.
	What are you studying?
	I'm studying economics.
Express ambition	I want a more challenging job.
Spell your name and address	C.L.A.P.H.A.M.
Say goodbye	Bye for now./Bye Bye.

WORDS AND EXPRESSIONS

art	buy	challenging	Bye for now!
college	call	fizzy	I'm sure ...
day	come	good	Let's meet ...
drink	go	interesting	not really
economics	like	part-time	OK
evening class	live	same	sort of
ice cream	meet		Thank you.
job	phone	during	That's all right.
lodger	say	here	That's why ...
neighbour	study	later	What about you?
telex	want	more	
operator		too	

VIEW AND ANSWER

I. Answer the questions.

Who 1. has a can of Coke?

Eddy (has a can of coke)

2. is wearing a cardigan?

....

3. has blonde hair?

....

4. is eating ice cream?

....

....

Where 5. does Lisa sit?

....

....

What 6. does Maribel take from her bag?

....

....

CHECK

2. Answer the questions.

Who 1. go to the same college?

<u>Lisa and Maribel (go to the</u>
<u>same college)</u>

2. is a telex operator?

....

3. is Lisa's lodger?

....

4. wants to make a phone call?

....

....

What 5. is Maribel studying?

....

....

6. is Eddy studying?

....

....

7. does Eddy want to do later?

....

....

8. are Judd and Potter doing in Covent
Garden?

....

Where 9. does Eddy's sister live?

....

10. do Lisa and Maribel live?

....

EXPLAIN

– why Lisa says 'So you're Eddy.'
– why Lisa says 'I'll see you in a minute. I want to
make a phone call.'

VIEW AND LISTEN FOR DETAIL

3. Complete the conversations.

`09.12`

1. **Eddy:** What are you studying Maribel?

Maribel: <u>I am studying</u> ....

....

What about you?

Eddy: I'm at .... Southampton.

I'm .... and ....

`09.56`

2. **Eddy:** What's your address?

Maribel: The address is ....

....

Eddy: Phone number?

Maribel: The number is ....

Eddy: 0.2.3. OK, well, um, I'll phone about seven
o'clock, if that's OK?

Maribel: Yes, ...

Eddy: Great. Well, ...

ROLEPLAY

Roleplay similar conversations to those above. Say
your name, address and phone number, and say
what you do or where you go to college.

GRAMMAR PRACTICE

PRESENT SIMPLE		
Does she like fizzy drinks?	Yes, she does.	
	No, she doesn't.	
She	likes	fizzy drinks.
	doesn't like	

4. Use the words to make questions and short answers using the present simple.

1. Maribel/like fizzy drinks? *Does Maribel like fizzy drinks?*
No, she doesn't.

2. Maribel/study economics? ....
....
....

3. Eddy/study in Oxford? ....
....
....

4. Annie/live in Clapham? ....
....
....

5. Annie/work in a shop? ....
....
....

6. Lisa/like ice cream? ....
....
....

5. Now write full sentences for each answer.

1. *Maribel doesn't like fizzy drinks.*

2. ....
....

3. ....
....

4. ....
....

5. ....
....

6. ....
....

WORD STUDY

6. Match the words in each column to make occupations. Use each word once only.

1. traffic — assistant

2. bank — operator

3. police — teacher

4. telex → warden

5. office — driver

6. bus — officer

7. shop — manager

8. school — worker

WRITE

7. Complete the information in the form and letters below.

1. Maribel's form for the Home Office.

Family name: ..Garcia............

First name: ....

Mr/Mrs/Miss/Ms   Age: ..20.........

Address in Britain: ....

....

Telephone number: ....

Place of study: Clapham-Battersea

Adult Education...........................

Institute...................................

Subject of study: ....

....

Number of hours study a week: .15..........

2. Eddy's letter of application for a job.

Dear Sir,

I would like to apply for the job you advertised in the Daily News on June 16th.

My name is ....

and I am 19 years old. I am at .... in

.... I am studying

.... and .... and

I am doing a .... on

.... at the moment.

3. Lisa's letter to a friend.

Dear Katie,
Sorry this letter is so late! Let me tell you my news. I've got a job as a ....
.... It isn't very .... I really would like a more ....
job. In fact I'm studying ....
at college at the moment. I'm only a .... student. I go to ....
classes. It's quite fun because my friend .... and I both go to
the ...... college. She's .... but her English is very good. She's a
.... in our house.
Anyway, must go now. Good luck with YOUR new job.
            Love,
            Lisa

DISCUSS

Are there places like Covent Garden in your city? If so, where are they? Do you like going there? Why (not)?

15

PREVIEW

Who are the two men in the picture?
What are they doing?
Why are they there?

Take my tuna.

I don't like fish.

LANGUAGE USE

Ask what people want	Do you want your tea?
	Don't you want sugar?
Talk about likes and dislikes	I don't like fish.
	I don't like jogging.
	I hope you like chocolate.
Talk about age	I'm too old for it.
	Too old! You're only twenty-one, aren't you?
Ask and talk about money	How much is (all) this?
	How much do I owe you?
	Eighty-five pence for the sandwich.
	That's one pound and thirty-two pence.
	I'll pay you later.
Apologise	I'm sorry about that.
	I hope it's OK.
Accept apologies	That's OK.

WORDS AND EXPRESSIONS

find out	cheese	I hope it's OK.
go jogging	chocolate	I'm sorry.
lose weight	fish	That's OK.
owe	pickle	
pay	salad	
try (to do something)	sandwich	
	sugar	
	tea	
	tuna	

VIEW AND ANSWER

I. Answer the questions.

1. Who is sitting in the car?

Potter (is sitting in the car)

2. What's he doing?

....

3. What does the traffic warden do?

....

....

4. What is Judd carrying?

....

....

5. Where does Eddy go?

....

....

6. Who knocks Eddy over?

....

....

CHECK

2. Number the pictures in the correct order.

a)

I'm sorry about that.

Number ....

Number ....

c)

d)

I hope you like chocolate.

Number ....

b)

How much do I owe you?

Number ....

Number ....

VIEW AND LISTEN FOR DETAIL

3. Complete the bill and add up the total.

`12.28`

```
Sandwich:      .....
Tea:           .....
Chocolate:     .....

Total:         .........
```

4. Who said the following? Tick the correct person.

1. `11.47` I don't like pickle.

   Eddy   Judd   Potter ✓

2. `12.03` Don't you want sugar?

   Judd   Lisa   Potter

3. `12.29` How much do I owe you?

   Potter   Eddy   Judd

4. `13.12` I hope it's OK.

   Skater   Judd   Eddy

5. Complete the conversation.

`11.53`

Judd: Here, *do you want your tea?*

Potter: Ugh! Sugar!

Judd: They've both got sugar. Don't you want sugar?

Potter: ....
All this sitting in cars makes you fat.

Judd: Not me. I go jogging.

Potter: ....
I'm too old for it.

Judd: Too old! ....,
aren't you?

Potter: Wish I was.

Judd: I hope you like chocolate.

Potter: How much ....

Judd: Eh?

Potter: .... do I owe you?

WORD STUDY

6. Label the kinds of food with the words from the box.

cheese	fish	fizzy drinks	fruit
meat	sweet things	vegetables	

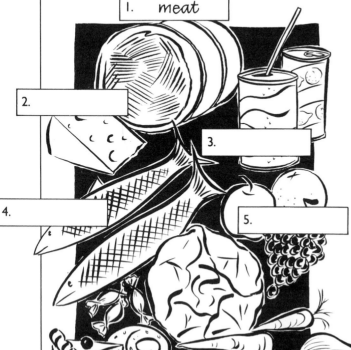

1. meat

2.

3.

4.

5.

6.

7.

7. Respond to these offers as in the example. Use the words in the box.

1. Would you like a nice steak?

No thanks. I don't like meat.

2. There's blue cheese, Cheddar and fetta.

....

3. We've got Pepsi, Coke and Fanta.

....

4. Have some chocolate cake.

....
....

5. Here, have an apple.

....

6. These are tuna sandwiches.

....

7. Do you want some peas and carrots?

....
....

GRAMMAR PRACTICE

VERBS FOLLOWED BY -ING
Do you like jogging?

TOO + ADJECTIVE + INFINITIVE
I'm too old to go jogging.

8. Use the words below each picture to ask the people if they like what they are doing.

1. (roller skate) ..Do..
you like
roller skating ?

2. (jog) ....
....
....

3. (listen to music).........
....
....

4. (drive) ....
....
....

5. (study English)...........
....
....

6. (ski) ....
....
....

9. Choose one of the adjectives in the box below to complete the sentences. You can use some adjectives more than once.

| cold   fat   hot   ill   old   tired   young |

1. I feel too ..**tired**...... to watch the late-night film.

2. The man was too .... to go to work.

3. It was too .... to sit in the sun.

4. I think you're too .... to wear so much make-up.

5. It's too .... to go swimming.

6. Dad, you're too .... to wear jeans.

7. I'm too .... to do my homework.

8. I'm too .... to wear these trousers. I must lose some weight.

WRITE

'All this sitting in cars makes you fat.'
10. In your notebook, write about why you think Mr Potter is overweight.

DISCUSS

What sort of home life do you think Mr Potter has? Talk about the sort of food and drink he likes, and the sort of things he likes doing in his spare time.

THE STORY

I. Rewrite the story so far and correct the mistakes. There are 10 altogether.

One day in summer Freddy Taylor, a student from Bristol, arrives by coach to spend the weekend in London. He wants to film some street fashion for a college project. He is going to stay at his sister's house in Waterloo, in South London, while she is away on business. His sister, Annie, works for a high security government office and he goes straight there from the airport to collect the keys to her flat. By mistake, he picks up the wrong keys.

Unaware of his mistake, Eddy goes to Trafalgar Square with his video camera to film some street fashion. There he meets a Mexican girl, Maribel, and her English friend, Lisa. They also live in Clapham and he arranges to meet them for a meal later.

In the meantime, Annie's boss, Mr Judd, has found that the keys to the top security filing cabinet in Annie's office are missing ...

One day in summer Eddy Taylor,

GRAMMAR

2. Look at Maribel's letter to a friend. Write the correct form of the verb in brackets.

London (be) .... a wonderful city.
The people (be) .... very nice. I
(stay) .... with my friend, Lisa,
and her husband, John. They (live) ....
.... in Clapham. I (be) ....
their lodger. You ask me what I (do) ....
.... here. Well, I (study) ....
.... economics at the same college
as Lisa. Our teacher is very good but
sometimes she (not like)...................
my English spelling!
By the way, (like / your family)...........
...................English tea? Let me know –
there (be) .... lots of different
sorts here and it (be) .... very cheap.

3. Fill in *he, she, his* **or** *her* **in these sentences.**

Eddy is a student of art and fashion. ...He...........

comes from Southampton. .... sister,

Annie, lives in London. .... says Eddy can

stay in .... flat while .... is away

on holiday. When .... meets Maribel,

.... films her with .... video

camera. Later, ... writes ....

address and telephone number on a piece of paper.

4. Draw an arrow between the question or remark and the correct response.

1. Good afternoon.   a) They're on the desk.

2. How do you do?   b) We're from Canada.

3. Where are the keys?   c) It's 896 3546.

4. What are you   d) Good afternoon.
   studying?

5. Where are you   e) I'm a traffic warden.
   staying?

6. How much is this?   f) Pleased to meet you.

7. Where are you   g) I'm studying modern
   from?   languages.

8. What do you do?   h) I'm staying with my
                             brother.

9. What's your   i) It's two pounds
   telephone number?   altogether.

LANGUAGE USE

5. Watch Unit 5 and complete the bubbles. Choose sentences from the list below.

The door keys are on the desk.
Where are the keys?
Hello. I'm Eddy. I'm from Southampton.
67 Listowel Road. L.I.S.T.O.W.E.L. The number is 223 5023.
I'm studying art and fashion.
I don't know. Perhaps my brother has them.

Hello. I'm Eddy. I'm from Southampton.

CROSSWORD

Across

1. Eddy is wearing an old one. (6)
4. Eddy asks Maribel: 'Can I ... you later?' (4)
6. Two ... in summer. (4)
8. Not he. (3)
9. Eddy is studying ... and fashion. (3)
10. Lisa is a ... operator. (5)
12. 'She is buying ice ...' (5)
14. Where ... you live? (2)
15. Not short. (4)
16. Potter doesn't like exercise so he ... in the car. (4)
18. Annie isn't pleased because Eddy is ... (4)
20. Eddy is carrying a video ... (6)
21. A number. (3)

Down

2. Lisa ... Maribel live in Clapham too. (3)
3. Eddy takes the wrong ... from Annie's office. (4)
5. Eddy's jacket is made of this. (7)
7. Maribel is wearing black ... (5)
11. 'It's ..., not Freddy.' (4)
12. Eddy comes to Annie's office to ... the keys. (7)
13. 'I ... go now, Eddy. That is my friend, Lisa.' (4)
15. Eddy travels by this when he comes to London. (5)
16. Lisa and Maribel study at the ... college. (4)
17. Eddy is going to ... at his sister's flat. (4)
19. Eddy arrives ... Waterloo Station. (2)

BACKGROUND

The 'V and A' is the popular name for the Victoria and Albert Museum, the national museum of art and design. It contains several million examples of decorative arts, including sculptures, ceramics, furniture and a magnificent dress collection. The museum is named after Queen Victoria and her husband, Prince Albert, who was a great patron of the arts in the mid-nineteenth century.

LANGUAGE USE

Ask and talk about past events	It was free the last time I came.
	When was that?
	That was three years ago.
	He left a few minutes ago.
Ask for and give directions	Which way to the dress collection?
	Through here, turn left, Room 40, on the right.
	Out through here, along the corridor.
Ask and say where you buy things	Where can I buy some postcards?
	At the shop.
	Do you sell stamps?
	There's a stamp machine on Waterloo Station.
	Is there anywhere else I can buy stamps?
Ask and talk about times	What time is it?
	It's twenty past five.
	We close in thirty minutes.
	Are you open tomorrow?
	We're open from ten o'clock until ten to six.

WORDS AND EXPRESSIONS

buy	along	machine	a few minutes ago
close	at (+ time)	railway	by the way
enter	in (+ time)	stamp	Don't worry.
get in	left	station	Hurry up.
leave	near		on my way
sell	out	free	via Waterloo
send	right	open	Station
turn	through		
	to (+ time)	Monday	
	tomorrow	Tuesday	
		Wednesday	
		Thursday	
		Friday	
		Saturday	
		Sunday	

VIEW AND ANSWER

I. Circle a, b or c.

1. Eddy is going into
   a) a church.
   b) a museum.
   c) Waterloo Station.

2. The man at the desk
   a) doesn't think Eddy is dressed correctly.
   b) tells Eddy that the museum is closing.
   c) wants Eddy to pay an entrance fee.

3. The man is
   a) pleasant to Eddy.
   b) angry with Eddy.
   c) rude to Eddy.

4. He directs Eddy to
   a) the exit.
   b) the dress collection.
   c) the cafeteria.

5. Eddy
   a) is trying to escape from Judd and Potter.
   b) doesn't know that Judd and Potter are following him.
   c) is following Judd and Potter.

CHECK

2. Number the pictures in the correct order.

a)

> Hurry up, we close soon.

Number ....

c)

> He left a few minutes ago. He said he was going to Clapham via Waterloo Station.

Number ....

Number ....

b)

> These are fifteen pence each. That's sixty pence.

d)

> I thought it was free to get in.

> It is, but there's a voluntary contribution.

Number ....

3. Answer the questions.

1. When did Eddy last visit the V and A?

(He last visited the V and A)
Three years ago

2. In which room is the dress collection?

3. What does Eddy buy at the V and A shop?

4. What time does the V and A close?

5. What else does he want to buy?

6. What's the matter with the stamp machine?

7. Where is there another stamp machine?

EXPLAIN

– why you think Eddy is filming eighteenth century fashion.
– how much you have to pay to get into the museum.
– how Judd and Potter know where Eddy is going.

VIEW AND LISTEN FOR DETAIL

4. Who said the following?

1. `17.59` Through here, turn left, Room 40, on the right.

The receptionist at the V and A.

2. `18.11` Hurry up, we close soon.

....

3. `18.49` Do you sell stamps?

....

4. `19.45` He left a few minutes ago.

....

5. Fill in the opening and closing times of the museum.

`19.11`

VICTORIA & ALBERT MUSEUM

SOUTH KENSINGTON.
LONDON SW7 2RL

Hours of opening:

Mondays to Thursdays and Saturdays

.... to ....

Sundays

.... to ....

Admission by Donation

Closed ....Christmas Eve.
Christmas Day, Boxing Day, New
Years Day and May Day Bank Holiday.

GRAMMAR PRACTICE

PAST SIMPLE WITH *AGO*

He left a few minutes/hours/weeks/months/years ago.

6. Imagine it is 5.35 pm on Saturday, June 13th 1987. Use the notes about the characters to make questions and answers in the past simple. Use a time phrase with *ago* in each answer.

Who?	What?	When?
1. Eddy	went on a school trip to the V and A	1984
2. Eddy	left museum	5.30 pm
3. Maribel	arrived in England	April 1987
4. Annie	booked her ticket to Corfu	May
5. Judd and Potter	started to follow Eddy	2 pm

1. *When did Eddy go on a school trip to the V and A? (He went) Three years ago.*

2. ....

....

....

3. ....

....

....

4. ....

....

....

5. ....

....

....

....

WORD STUDY

7. Number each diagram with the correct directions.

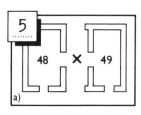
a)

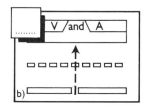
b)

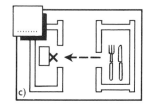
c)

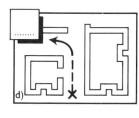
d)

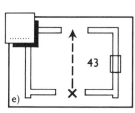
e)

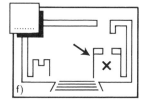
f)

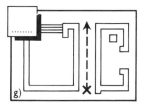
g)

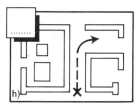
h)

1. Turn left.
2. Go through Room 43.
3. Cross over Cromwell Road.
4. Turn right.
5. It's between Room 48 and Room 49.
6. Go along this corridor.
7. It's opposite the cafeteria.
8. It's next to the exit.

ROLEPLAY

Look at the map of the area around the Victoria and Albert Museum and the information about how to find the museum. Work in pairs.

1. You are outside South Kensington underground station. You want to walk to the V and A. Ask for directions. Then ask what the time is and what time the museum closes.

2. You are inside the V and A. A man asks you where the Science Museum is. Look at the map and tell him. He also wants to know if there is a shop in the V and A which sells posters.

WRITE

8. In your notebook, write a postcard from the dress collection to an English friend. Say what the museum and dress exhibition were like and what your plans are.

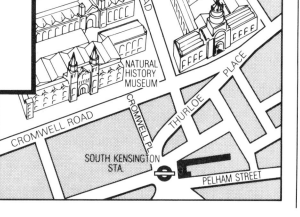

HOW TO FIND THE
MUSEUM

The museum is on the corner of Exhibition Road and Cromwell Road. Underground to South Kensington Station. Buses 14, 30 and 74 stop outside the museum. There is no car park.

PREVIEW

Who are the people in the photo?
Where are they?
What are they doing?
What sort of information is in the
personal file?

Just a few more questions, Miss Taylor.

LANGUAGE USE

Ask and talk about present activities	What's he doing? He's heading for Clapham. Mr Judd is following him.
Ask and talk about routines and habits	I start at nine and I leave at four thirty. Do you drive to work? No, I take the underground. It takes about half an hour.
Talk about personal details	I've got no boyfriend – and no pets. My father died three years ago. I live alone.
Ask and talk about present states	How long have you been with us? (I've been with you) Just over a year.

WORDS AND EXPRESSIONS

die	beach	Just a few more ...
drive	boyfriend	We'll see.
follow	cold	
head for	job	
live	month	
tell	pet	
	sunshine	
alone	time off	
apart from	underground	
before	work	
	year	

VIEW AND ANSWER

I. Answer Yes or No.

Annie

1. is still at Kent House. ...Yes.........

2. looks pleased. ....

3. is interested in Mr Archer's questions.

    ....

Mr Archer

4. is interviewing Annie for a job. ....

5. has her file in front of him on the desk.

    ....

6. is friendly and polite to Annie. ....

Eddy

7. goes up the escalator to the underground.

    ....

8. sends his postcard by first class post. ....

Judd

9. is following Eddy by car. ....

CHECK

2. Answer the questions.

1. Who was on the phone to Mr Archer?

Judd (was on the phone to
Mr Archer).

2. Where does Annie say Eddy is going?

....

....

3. What is Mr Potter doing while Mr Archer is talking to Annie?

....

4. How many are there in Annie's family?

....

5. When did her father die?

....

6. Has Annie ever been to Spain?

....

EXPLAIN

– why Mr Archer asks so many questions.
– why Judd doesn't arrest Eddy on the escalator.

VIEW AND LISTEN FOR DETAIL

3. Circle the words which you think you heard.

1. `20.58` Archer: How long (have you been)/ will you be with us?

2. `21.03` Archer: Yes, fourteen/forty months and one week.

3. `21.22` Archer: You've got/You've just one brother ... Eddy?

4. `21.33` Annie: I live on my own/alone. I've got no boyfriend – and no pets.

4. Complete this paragraph about Annie.

`28.50`

Annie Taylor works in Kent House, a high security government office. She has worked there for

one year......., ... months and

.... She starts work at .... and finishes at .... She leaves home at .... and her journey by .... takes her about

.... She is not .... very often apart from one or two .... Her

.... lives in Southampton, her father

.... three years ago and she ....

one brother. She lives .... in Clapham. She has .... boyfriend and no ....

WORD STUDY

5. Look at the list of words below. Which words do you associate with

1. a summer holiday by the sea?
2. a winter holiday?
3. a sightseeing holiday?

Write 1, 2 or 3 next to each word. Then compare your answers with your partner's. Which words belong to more than one category?

...1...	beach	....	museum
....	bikini	....	sand
....	camera	....	skiing
....	castle	....	slalom
....	comfortable shoes	....	snow
....	guide	....	sunglasses
....	map	....	sunshine
....	mountain	....	swimming

GRAMMAR PRACTICE

PRESENT PERFECT

How long have you been in this class?
I've been in this class for ten weeks.

6. In pairs have a conversation. Ask a question in the present simple and follow it with a question in the present perfect starting with _How long ..._

1. Where do you live?

I live in Munich.
How long have you lived there?
I've lived there for five years.

2. Where do you go to school?
3. Where do you work?
4. Are you married?
5. Have you got any pets?

Write the conversations in the space below.

2. You: *Where do you go to school?*

Your friend: ....

....

You: ....

....

Your friend: ....

....

3. You: ....

Your friend: ....

You: ....

....

Your friend: ....

....

4. You: ....

Your friend: ....

You: ....

....

Your friend: ....

....

5. You: ....

Your friend: ....

You: ....

....

Your friend: ....

....

7. In your notebook, write a few sentences about your partner like this:

Carla has lived in Treviso for ten years. She lives in a flat in the centre of town. She has lived there for three years. She isn't married and she has no pets/she hasn't got any pets.

WRITE

8. Complete the charts with details of your daily routine and your annual holidays.

▶ROUTINE◀

★ Name:

★ Place of work/study:

★ Means of transport there and back:

★ Departure time from home: _____ am/pm

★ Arrival time: _____ am/pm

★ Hours of work/study: from   to

★ Days:

● HOLIDAYS

☆ Number of days per year:

☆ Season:

☆ Destination/s:

☆ Reason for choice:

9. In your notebook, write about yourself, your daily routine and your annual holidays. Use the information in the charts.

10. In your notebook, write Annie's statement to Mr Archer explaining what has happened so far. Begin like this:

At twelve o'clock today my brother, Eddy Taylor, came to my office ...

DISCUSS

1. What is your favourite holiday place? Why?
2. How do you travel there? How long do you usually stay there?
3. Have you ever been to Britain or the USA? Why do people want to visit these countries?

PREVIEW

Where did Eddy go after posting his postcards?
Who is he talking to?
What do you think his problem is?

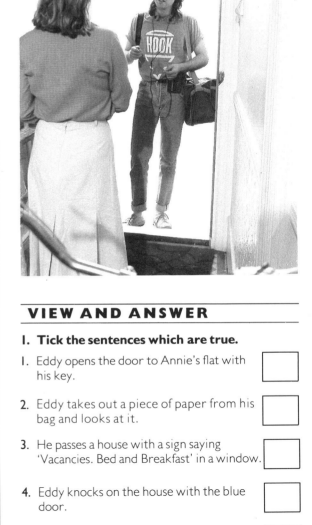

I've got a bit of a problem.

LANGUAGE USE

Talk about journeys	How did you get here?
	I walked.
	I usually cycle to the tube station.
	He goes by car.
	It's about an hour's drive each way.
Offer food and drink and hospitality	Would you like some tea?
	Would you like something to drink?
	Would you like to stay and eat with us?
	Why don't you stay here?
Accept offers	Yes, please.
	That would be nice, thank you.
Refuse offers with explanations	Thanks, but no. It's too much trouble.
	Thanks all the same.
Talk about the home	This is the spare room.
	It's going to be my study.
	We're decorating the house.
Make decisions	I'll stay at the guest house.

WORDS AND EXPRESSIONS

bedroom	book	Come in.
bike	cycle	I'm not sure.
guest house	decorate	I'm sorry to trouble you.
hole	do up	It'll be all right.
junk	get	Please do.
kitchen	show	See you in a minute.
(homemade)		
lemonade	quicker	
loft	usually	
problem		
sitting room		
spare room		
study		
trip		
trouble		
tube		
window		

VIEW AND ANSWER

I. Tick the sentences which are true.

1. Eddy opens the door to Annie's flat with his key. ☐

2. Eddy takes out a piece of paper from his bag and looks at it. ☐

3. He passes a house with a sign saying 'Vacancies. Bed and Breakfast' in a window. ☐

4. Eddy knocks on the house with the blue door. ☐

5. Maribel answers the door. ☐

6. There's a bicycle in the hall. ☐

CHECK

2. Number the pictures in the correct order.

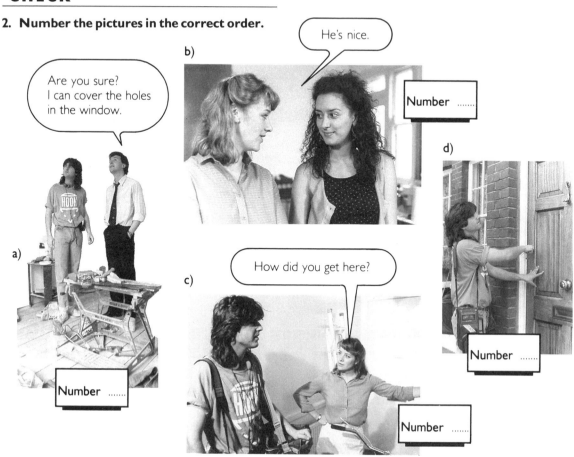

a)
Are you sure?
I can cover the holes in the window.

Number ....

b)
He's nice.

Number ....

c)
How did you get here?

Number ....

d)
Number ....

3. Correct the information.

1. Lisa cycles all the way to work.

Lisa cycles to the tube station

2. John goes to work by train.

....

3. John's journey takes two hours each way.

....
....

4. Lisa offers Eddy some coffee.

....
....

5. John shows Eddy the sitting room.

....
....

6. Eddy decides to stay with Lisa and John.

....
....

DESCRIBE OR EXPLAIN

– what the spare room looks like and why Eddy doesn't want to stay.
– what sort of people you think John and Lisa are: friendly? rich? typically British?
– any differences between English houses and houses in your country.

VIEW AND LISTEN FOR DETAIL

4. Who said the following, to whom and about what?

1. **24.00** I've got a bit of a problem.

Eddy to Lisa, about having the wrong keys to his sister's flat.

2. **25.30** Oh! What's he going to do?

....

....

3. **26.14** That would be nice. Thank you.

....

....

4. **26.43** You've got plenty of work to do.

....

....

5. **27.12** Thanks but no. No, it's too much trouble.

....

....

WORD STUDY

5. Look at the list of words below. Which words do you associate with

1. the kitchen?   3. the sitting room?
2. the bathroom?   4. the bedroom?

Write 1, 2, 3 or 4 next to each word.

..3.. armchair	.... fridge
.... bath	.... oven
.... bed	.... sink
.... bookshelf	.... sofa
.... coffee table	.... toilet
.... desk	.... TV
.... dressing table	.... wardrobe
.... freezer	.... washbasin

6. Look at the photograph of the kitchen table. Write a list of what you can see on the table.

knives, ...

....

....

GRAMMAR PRACTICE

MODAL VERB *WOULD* FOR INVITATIONS
Would you like some tea?

7. Circle the appropriate response to the offers and invitations.

1. Would you like something to drink?
   a) Yes, I like orange juice.
   b) Yes, please. Some orange juice would be nice.

2. Would you like some coffee?
   a) No thanks.
   b) Yes, I'd love to.

3. Would you like some fruit?
   a) Yes, I'd love some. Thank you.
   b) Yes, I do. Thank you.

4. Why don't you stay the night with us?
   a) No thanks.
   b) Thanks but no. It's too much trouble. Thanks all the same.

5. Would you like to freshen up in the bathroom?
   a) Thanks but no. It's too much trouble.
   b) Yes, that would be nice, thank you.

WILL + INFINITIVE

I'll stay at the bed and breakfast.

8. Make decisions in the following situations:

1. You are at Waterloo Station. It is 11.30 pm and the last train to Clapham has already gone.

I'll take a taxi. ....

....

2. You decide to have a party at the weekend.

....

....

3. It is after midnight and your neighbour who lives upstairs is playing music very loudly.

....

....

4. Your mother wants you to telephone her this evening but you are too tired when you get in from work.

....

....

WRITE

9. You are Eddy. In your notebook, write a note to Lisa and John thanking them for helping you when you were in trouble. Say how much you enjoyed the meal. Say you hope the decorating is going well and add a message for Maribel.

DISCUSS

1. How do you get to and from class? How long does it take you?
2. Would you invite a stranger into your home?
3. Are all landladies and landlords as friendly with their lodgers as Lisa and John?

OPEN DIALOGUE

10. You are in London and decide to visit Lisa whom you met when you last visited England. Complete the conversation.

Lisa: Oh, hello. What a surprise! How nice to see you again. Come in.

You: *Thank you.* ....

Lisa: What are you doing in London?

You: ....

....

Lisa: How did you get here?

You: ....

....

Lisa: Come on through to the sitting room.

You: ....

....

Lisa: Would you like some tea?

You: ....

Lisa: With milk and sugar?

You: ....

Lisa: Look! Why don't you stay for dinner?

You: ....

....

ROLEPLAY

Roleplay a similar conversation. Invite a friend into your home and offer food and drink according to the time of day and your custom.

PREVIEW

What is John doing? .
Who do you think he is talking to?
What is he talking about?

> It's not on until nine thirty.
> What shall we do until then?

LANGUAGE USE

Talk on the telephone	Hello. Can I speak to Mr Archer?
	It's Mr Judd.
	Judd speaking.
	Can you ask him to call me back?
Ask and talk about plans	It's Sunday tomorrow. What are you all doing?
	I'm going to the V and A in the afternoon.
	I've got a bit of decorating to do.
Invite people to do things	Would you like to come sightseeing with me?
Accept invitations	Yes, I'd like that.
Ask for and make suggestions	What shall we do until then?
	Shall we watch television?
	Let's watch that (documentary).
Give an opinion with a reason	It's boring.
	I didn't like it. It was too violent.

WORDS AND EXPRESSIONS

boring	call back	That sounds like fun!
criminal	check into	What else is there?
interesting	help	What's on?
political	own	
violent		
	architect	
	record	
	sightseeing	

VIEW AND ANSWER

I. Answer the questions.

Where 1. is Judd? ..(He's).. In the car.

      2. are Maribel, Lisa, John and Eddy?

....

....

      3. are Maribel and Eddy sitting?

....

....

What 4. is John's job? ....

....

      5. does Judd eat? ....

....

      6. do you think Maribel, Lisa, John and Eddy are talking about?

....

....

CHECK

2. Circle the right answer.

1. Archer wants Judd and Potter
   a) to bring Eddy to see him.
   b) to stop following Eddy.
   c) to continue following Eddy.

2. Lisa
   a) doesn't like football.
   b) doesn't mind football.
   c) likes football even when it's boring.

3. They decide to watch
   a) a football match.
   b) a Clint Eastwood film.
   c) a wildlife film.

4. The programme they want to watch
   a) is just going to start.
   b) started at 9.30.
   c) starts at 9.30.

3. Complete the information in the chart below.

Plans for Sunday	Morning
John	decorate
Lisa	
Eddy	
Maribel	
	Afternoon
John	
Lisa	
Eddy	
Maribel	

EXPLAIN

– why Eddy is staying at a guest house.
– why Potter says 'That's only forty-seven pence I owe you.'
– how you think Judd found out the information about Lisa and John.

VIEW AND LISTEN FOR DETAIL

4. Who said the following to whom?

1. **28.01** Can you ask him to call me back?
   Judd to Archer's assistant

2. **29.22** A bit? You've got a whole house to do!
   ....

3. **29.53** No, not football, it's boring.
   ....

4. **30.27** Me? On TV?
   ....

5. Complete Judd's notes about Lisa and John.

28.20

MRS LISA HARRIS

BORN   19

MR JOHN HARRIS

BORN   19

6. Complete the conversations.

27.57

1. Judd: Hello. Can I speak to ......
   Mr Archer? .... Mr Judd. Can you
   ask him to...
   (*to Potter*) He's checked into the guest house.

   Judd: .... Yes, Mr Archer.
   He ....
   .... in Clapham.

29.36

2. Eddy: ....,
   Maribel?
   Maribel: Oh, no, I don't think so.
   Eddy: ....
   ....
   with me?
   Maribel: ....
   Eddy: Great!

37

WORD STUDY

7. Look at the TV guide and find examples of the kind of programmes listed below. Write the name of the programme and the time it starts.

ITV LONDON

6.15 GOOD MORNING BRITAIN.
9.25 THAMES NEWS.
9.30 SCHOOLS: Stop, Look, Listen 'A'. 9.42 Time for a Story. 9.54 All Year Round. 10.11 Picture Box. 10.28 Your Living Body. 10.45 Craft, Design and Technology '5'. 11.3 Middle English. 11.20 Talk, Write . . . and Read. 11.37 How We Used to Live.
12.0 THOMAS THE TANK ENGINE AND FRIENDS (rpt).
12.10 PUDDLE LANE (rpt).
12.30 THE SULLIVANS: Jim sprains an ankle.
1.0 NEWS. 1.20 THAMES NEWS.
1.30 LEVKAS MAN: Part 6 (rpt).
2.25 HOME COOKERY CLUB.
2.30 DAYTIME: The Jarrow Marchers.
3.0 TAKE THE HIGH ROAD: Inverdarroch sets out to clear his name.
3.25 THAMES NEWS.
3.30 SONS AND DAUGHTERS: Fiona is touched by Terry's bid to cheer her up.
4.0 FLICKS: Stories about a steam shovel and a scarecrow.
4.10 THE TRAP DOOR: Lurkings.
4.20 ANIMALS IN ACTION, with Vicky Licorish and Mike Linley.
4.45 CHOCKY'S CHALLENGE: Part 4. Albertine and her friends have problems keeping their plans secret.
5.15 BLOCKBUSTERS: Teenage quiz.
5.45 NEWS. 6.0 THAMES NEWS.

6.25 HELP! Why the National Health Service needs volunteer drivers to take patients to hospital.
6.35 CROSSROADS.
7.0 EMMERDALE FARM: Is Sandie's marriage really on the rocks?
7.30 FRESH FIELDS (T): Caught in the Act. Hester (Julia McKenzie) invites Emma's in-laws to dinner and regrets it when they announce they'll be staying the night.
8.0 FILM: The Runaway Train (1973). Passengers with a dramatic variety of troubles on their minds see death as the common solution as they hurtle down a mountainside on a brakeless train. Starring Ben Johnson, Vera Miles, Ben Murphy and Ed Nelson.
9.30 THIS WEEK: See Pick of the Day.
10.0 NEWS AT TEN, Thames News.
10.30 THAMES SPORT SPECIAL: Some of Britain's brightest young hopes are in action at the Fairfield Halls, Croydon, as the programme covers professional boxing's Stars of the Future.
11.45 KOJAK: Cross Your Heart and Hope to Die. Kojak has double trouble – with a mental patient who cannot cope with the reality of a murder she has witnessed, and with the murderer.
12.40 NIGHT THOUGHTS; CLOSE.

Type	Name	Time
A soap opera	Crossroads	6.35
A sports programme		
A wildlife programme		
A news programme		
A documentary		
A quiz show		
A film		
A comedy series	Fresh Fields	
A crime series		

8. Use the TV programmes above to practise conversations like this:

A: Shall we watch television?
B: OK. What's on?
A: There's a wildlife programme called 'Animals in Action'.
B: No, not a wildlife programme. That's boring. What else is there?
A: There's ...
B: What time does it start?
A: ...
B: OK. Let's watch that.

GRAMMAR PRACTICE

PRESENT PERFECT/PAST SIMPLE

Have you seen *Dirty Harry*?
Yes, I have. I saw it last Saturday at the Odeon.
Did you like it?
No, I didn't. It was too violent.

9. Look at the list of opinions.

I thought it was (really) good/great/funny/
    boring/exciting.
It was one of the best/worst/funniest/most exciting
    films I have ever seen.
I liked/hated it.

**Think of a film you have seen recently. Follow
the cues below to write a conversation about
it.**

A: Ask your friend if he/she has seen (name of film).

A: *Have you seen Dirty Harry?*

B: Say you have. Say when you saw it and where.

B: ....

....

A: Ask if he/she liked it.

A: ....

B: Say you didn't. Say what you thought of it.

B: ....

....

A: Disagree. Say what you thought of it.

A: ....

....

....

ROLEPLAY

Telephone a friend and ask about his/her plans for
Saturday evening. Suggest a good film and arrange
a time and place to meet.

Are you busy tomorrow, Maribel?

WRITE

**10. Imagine you have just returned from a
week's holiday in London or another big city.
In your notebook, write a letter to a friend
telling him or her what you did while you were
there and what you thought of the city. You
can comment on the people, the food, any
places you visited and any shows or films you
saw.**

DISCUSS

1. Talk about TV programmes which you like and
   watch regularly. Say why you like them.
2. Do you think some films and TV programmes
   are too violent? Which ones?
3. What sort of film censorship do you have in
   your country? Do you think it is a sensible
   system? Does it work?

THE STORY

1. Fill in the gaps in the text.

When Mr Archer finds that **the keys to the top security filing cabinet**

(What?) are missing, he immediately suspects

.... (Who?). Annie tells Archer

that she knows nothing about the keys but

thinks that perhaps ....

(Who?) took them, thinking they were her

.... (Which?) keys. Archer

orders two security policemen, Mr Judd and Mr Potter, to .... (What?).

    After Covent Garden, Eddy goes to .... (Where?) and films the dress collection.

He then goes to .... (Where?) to catch a train to Clapham. When Eddy arrives

at his sister's flat, he finds of course that ....

(What?). He has .... (What?) in his pocket. He goes to her

house to see if she can help him with his problem. .... (Who?) invites him in and he

spends the evening there. Because John and Lisa are decorating ....

(What?), Eddy decides to spend the night .... (Where?).

2. Complete the information for Judd and Potter's report.

SD SECURITY DIVISION

SURVEILLANCE REPORT

Name: _Eddy Taylor_

Age: _____

Occupation: _____

Family relations: _____

Address: _27 Highview Road, Southampton, Hampshire_ TOP SECRET

Description: Hair: _____

    Clothes: _____

MOVEMENTS

SD SECURITY DIVISION

Saturday:
Went to Kent House to
collect keys. Then went to
ovent Garden. Met two
women. Went to _____ in
fternoon and filmed
ollection. _____ some
ostcards. Went to
ation. Posted a postcard.
_____ by _____ to
apham. Walked to
_____ Couldn't
Jent to _____ in Listowel
oad. Spent evening there.
ooked into _____ for
ne night.

REASON FOR SURVEILLANCE

e suspect he has stolen keys to
> security filing cabinet.

SD SECURITY DIVISION

CONTACTS

Name: *Maribel Garcia*

Nationality: _____

Occupation: _____

Address: _____

ACTS **SD** SECURITY DIVISION

hn + Lisa Harris

: _____

: _____

GRAMMAR

3. Circle the correct answer to go into the dialogue.

Lisa is shopping in Clapham and meets an old school friend.

Jill: Hello, Lisa. What a surprise to see you! I ... you for ages.
a) (haven't seen) b) don't see c) have seen

Lisa: Yes. The last time ... at school.
a) is b) has been c) was

Jill: ... we go and have a cup of coffee?
a) Shall b) Will c) Here

Lisa: Yes. ... go to that cafe over there.
a) We b) Let's c) Why don't

Jill: OK. How's John, by the way?

Lisa: Fine. He ... the house at the moment.
a) decorated b) decorates
c) is decorating

Jill: Here we are. Oh no. It's closed. What's the time?

Lisa: Five past five. It closed ...
a) five minutes ago b) since five o'clock
c) for five minutes

Jill: What time ... the pubs open?
a) does b) did c) do

Lisa: About five thirty I think. But I really must go. John gets back from work soon.

Jill: Well, I really should go too. ... a lift home? I've got my car over there.
a) Do you like b) Would you like
c) You like

Lisa: Thanks but no. It's too much trouble. I ... catch a bus.
a) am b) 'll c) go

Jill: OK. Where's the nearest postbox by the way?

Lisa: Go ... the car park over there and there's one on the other side.
a) out b) along c) through

Jill: Great. Thanks. Hope to see you around.

Lisa: OK. Bye!

LANGUAGE USE

4. Watch Unit 10 and complete the bubbles. Choose sentences from the list below.

Where can I buy some postcards?
Would you like some tea?
It was free the last time I came.
Through here, turn left, Room 40, on the right.
We're open from ten o'clock until ten to six.
There's myself and Eddy. My mother lives in Southampton.

4.

1.

> It was free the last time I came.

2.

5.

3.

6.

CROSSWORD

Across

1. This was out of order at the V and A. (5, 7)
7. A car needs petrol and ... (3)
8. An acid fruit. (5)
10. Annie has no boyfriend and no ... (4)
11. Part of body. (3)
12. A sandy place near the sea. (5)
14. Short for Robert (3)
15. Annie lives ... (5)
17. Eddy stayed at a ... and breakfast. (3)
20. 5th and 6th letters of the alphabet. (2)
22. See you ... a minute. (2)
24. What ... does the museum close? (4)
25. Is this museum ... on Sunday? (4)
26. The spare room ... in John and Lisa's house has a hole in it. (6)

Down

1. What you need on a summer holiday (3)
2. That was three years ... (3)
3. Lisa has no criminal or ... record. (9)
4. Thanks ... the same. (3)
5. John offers Eddy some ... lemonade. (8)
6. In Britain most schools start at ... o'clock. (4)
9. A period of time (4)
10. Something difficult. (7)
13. John promises to cover this in the spare room. (4)
16. The house is ... by Lisa and John Harris. (5)
18. Why ... you stay here? (4)
19. The museum closes ... ten to six. (2)
21. He left a ... minutes ago. (3)
23. ... did you get here? (3)

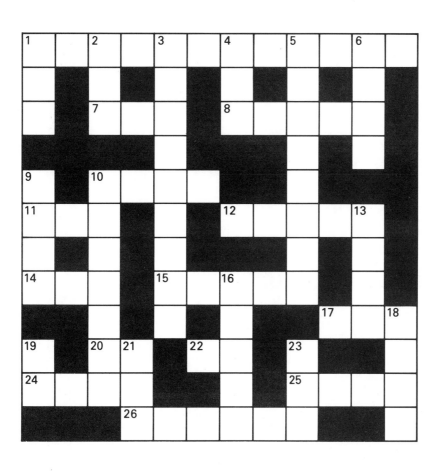

UNIT

BACKGROUND

The Thames Barrier is the world's largest moveable flood barrier and is a remarkable example of 20th century engineering. It consists of ten enormous steel gates which can be raised to dam the River Thames if there is danger of flooding from the North Sea. When they are raised, the four main gates are as high as a five-storey building. When the gates are in a normal lowered position, ships can go up and down the river freely.

LANGUAGE USE

Express appreciation	What a fabulous shop!
	Yeah, it's brilliant.
Ask and talk about size	Do you think this is big enough?
	Excuse me. Do you have larger T-shirts?
	Yes, we do small, medium and large.
	Can I see a large T-shirt, please?
Ask and talk about price	How much are these?
	The large ones are eight pounds.
	The smaller ones are five pounds fifty.
	How much is that altogether?
	That's fourteen pounds and fifty pence.
Ask and talk about buying and paying	Do you accept credit cards?
	I can take a traveller's cheque.
	I'll have the small one, please.

WORDS AND EXPRESSIONS

credit card	big	enough	Certainly.
duck	brilliant	later	Excuse me.
gift	fabulous	outside	He's back.
night	large	yet	I'm afraid not.
passport	medium		It makes
pen	ready		a change.
shop	small		They're off.
size			
traveller's cheque			

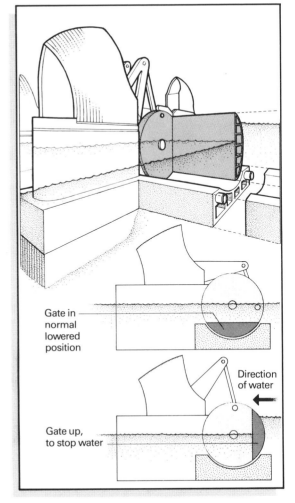

Gate in normal lowered position

Direction of water

Gate up, to stop water

VIEW AND ANSWER

I. Answer the questions.

1. What are these people doing at the beginning of the episode?

Judd .....*is shaving*.........................

Potter ....

....

Eddy ....

....

John, Lisa and Maribel ....

....

2. Where are Eddy and Maribel going and how do they get there?

....

....

....

3. What does Maribel buy in the shop?

....

....

CHECK

2. Describe what is happening in each picture, using the present continuous.

1. ....*Eddy is calling to collect*..........
Maribel.....................................

2. ....

....

3. ....
....
....
....

4. ....
....
....
....

5. ....

....

3. In your notebook, tell the story of the pictures above. Use the past simple.

4. Write True, False or Don't know against each statement.

1. Lisa and John have never been to the Thames Barrier before. ...True..........

2. Maribel has seen the Tower of London.

   ....

3. John invites Eddy back for a meal after the trip.

   ....

4. Maribel buys a T-shirt for Lisa too. ....

5. Eddy likes the crystal ducks. ....

6. Maribel pays cash for the gifts. ....

EXPLAIN OR DESCRIBE

– why Eddy says 'Well, it makes a change from the Tower of London and Trafalgar Square.'
– how you think Judd and Potter are feeling.
– how you think John and Lisa are going to spend their day.

VIEW AND LISTEN FOR DETAIL

5. Complete the conversation between Maribel and the souvenir shop assistant.

37.44

Maribel: Can I have a look ....
at those crystal ducks, please?

Assistant: Yes, certainly.

Maribel: How .... ?

Assistant: The .... are
eight pounds and the smaller ones are

....

Maribel: I'll have ...., please

How .... ?

Assistant: That's fourteen pounds and fifty pence.

Maribel: I haven't got enough. Um, ...

.... credit cards?

QUIZ

Be a detective! How many questions can you answer?

1. Was there a word or a picture on Eddy's T-shirt?
(There was) A picture.......................

2. Who opened the door to Eddy?

   ....

3. Were they drinking tea or coffee at breakfast?

   ....

4. What colour were Maribel's clothes?

   ....

   ....

5. What sort of bag was she carrying?

   ....

   ....

6. What was different about Judd's appearance?

   ....

7. What was there to see at the Thames Barrier Centre apart from the barrier itself and a shop?

   ....

WORD STUDY

6. Look at the list of words and phrases below. Sort them into three groups:

1. things which you use to keep money in.
2. things which are used instead of money.
3. money.

Write 1, 2 or 3 next to each word.

..2.. cheque   .... purse

.... coin   .... safe

.... credit card   .... 10p (pence) piece

.... dollar   .... ten pound note

.... money box   .... traveller's cheque

.... postal order   .... wallet

GRAMMAR PRACTICE

> ### NOT + ADJECTIVE + ENOUGH
>
> It's not large enough. Do you have a larger one?

7. Write a short dialogue to accompany each picture.

1. A: Can I help you?

   B: (long) Yes, I'm afraid these skis aren't long enough. Do you have any longer ones?

2. A: ....

   B: (big) ....

   ....

3. A: ....

   B: (cold) ....

   ....

   ....

4. A: ....

   B: (small) ....

   ....

   ....

OPEN DIALOGUE

8. Complete the conversation in a shop. You want to buy a T-shirt.

Assistant: Can I help you?

You: Yes. Can I have a look at those T-shirts, please?

Assistant: Certainly. What about this one?

You: ....

....

Assistant: Yes, we do small, medium and large.

You: ....

....

Assistant: Here you are. Is that better?

You: ....

....

Assistant: How are you going to pay?

You: ....

....

Assistant: That's fine. That'll be five pounds fifty please.

WRITE

9. Write Maribel's letter to an English friend, Louise, in Bristol. Say what you are doing and where you are staying. Tell her about Eddy and what you think of him. Mention some of the sights of London you have seen.

> ### DISCUSS
>
> Is there a modern tourist attraction in your country? Where is it and why is it interesting? When is the best time to visit it? What souvenirs can you buy there?

PREVIEW

Who are the people in the photo?
Where are they?
Where are they going?
What is Judd talking about?

It's certainly been a nice day, hasn't it?

LANGUAGE USE

Give orders	Tell him to bring the boy Eddy to see me.
	Don't bring the girl. Send her home.
	You must come with me.
	Get the car.
Confirm things	It's certainly been a nice day, hasn't it?
Ask about past activities	Did you go to the Thames Barrier?
	Did you enjoy your outing?
	Did you buy anything at the shop?
Narrate past events in sequence	We took a walk along the river and then we went on a boat trip.
Invite formally	Perhaps you'd like a lift?
Refuse invitations politely and firmly	Thank you for offering.
	It's very kind of you, but ...

WORDS AND EXPRESSIONS

boat	bring
choice	drop
lift	enjoy
outing	get (= fetch)
ride	offer
walk	wait

VIEW AND ANSWER

I. Answer the questions.

1. Where is Potter?

(He's sitting) In the car beside the River Thames.

2. Who does he talk to?

....

3. Where does Judd sit on the boat?

....
....

4. What does he take from his top pocket to show Eddy and Maribel?

....
....

CHECK

2. Answer the questions.

1. Who does Mr Archer want to see?

(He wants to see) Eddy.

2. What does he tell Potter to do with Maribel?

....

3. How does Judd open his conversation with Maribel and Eddy?

....

4. Did Judd eat at the restaurant?

....

5. What does Judd tell Maribel and Eddy to do?

....

....

3. Match the questions 1–5 with the correct responses a–e. Say who spoke the lines.

1. ...c)... 2. .... 3. .... 4. .... 5. ....

1. ....Potter.....: What about the girl?

2. ....: Did you enjoy your outing?

3. ....: How was the food?

4. ....: It's very kind of you, but ...

5. ....: It's certainly been a nice day, hasn't it?

a) ....: I'm afraid you have no choice.

b) ....: It was all right.

c) ....: No. Don't bring the girl. Send her home.

d) ....: Yes. Yes, it has.

e) ....: Yes, I did ... We did.

4. Number the sentences in the correct sequence and follow Eddy and Maribel's movements at the Thames Barrier on the map.

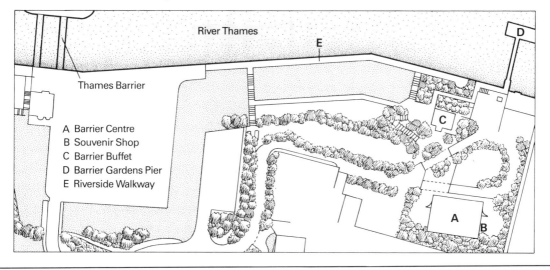

River Thames

E

D

Thames Barrier

A Barrier Centre
B Souvenir Shop
C Barrier Buffet
D Barrier Gardens Pier
E Riverside Walkway

C

A

B

.... After buying some presents, they had something to eat at the Barrier Buffet.

.... Then they walked along the Riverside Walk.

...1.... First they arrived by boat at the Barrier Gardens Pier and looked at the exhibition at the Barrier Centre.

.... Then they went into the Souvenir Shop and bought some presents.

.... Finally, they went back to the pier and caught the boat back to Westminster.

.... After their walk they went on a boat trip.

EXPLAIN

– how Maribel and Eddy react to Judd's questions.
– why Eddy and Maribel have to go with Judd.

VIEW AND LISTEN FOR DETAIL

5. Complete Judd's questions to Maribel and Eddy. Then read the conversation with a partner.

`41.26`

Judd:	I enjoy this boat ride along the Thames. Did ..*you go to the Thames Barrier*..?
Eddy:	Yeah. Did you?
Judd:	Yeah. ....
Maribel:	Yes, I did ... We did.
Judd:	.... shop?
Maribel:	Yes.
Judd:	I didn't eat at the restaurant. How .... food?
Eddy:	It was all right.

ROLEPLAY

Talk to a friend about a famous place you have both visited.
(Find a place of interest which you have both been to.)
Have you ever been to ...
(Find out when your partner visited the place.)
When did you go ...
(Find out if you saw the same things.)
Did you see ...
(Find out where they had refreshments.)
Where did you have ...
(Find out if they bought anything there.)
Did you buy ...

GRAMMAR PRACTICE

INDIRECT ORDERS

Tell him to fetch the boy.

6. Use your imagination. Make indirect orders from the table below as if one of the characters in the story was saying it. Your partner must guess who gave the order to whom.

Tell	Maribel Judd Potter Lisa John your brother	to	cover the holes in the window. fetch the car. buy some more paint. get me a T-shirt. follow them. bring the keys to Kent House immediately.

1. Tell Maribel to get me a T-shirt.
(John to Lisa or Eddy)

2. ....
....
....

3. ....
....
....

4. ....
....
....

5. ....
....
....

6. ....
....
....

WORD STUDY

7. Use the adjectives in the box and the words beneath the pictures to write what the people are saying.

delicious	fabulous	pretty
enormous	lovely	wide

4. (Thames Barrier) ....

....

5. (bracelets) ....

....

....

1. (Tower Bridge) Tower Bridge is fabulous, isn't it? ....

6. (river) ....

....

2. (strawberries) ....

....

WRITE

8. Imagine that the police have arrested you on a false charge. Write a statement of your movements over the last forty-eight hours.

DISCUSS

1. Do you ever talk to strangers? When?
2. What sort of things make a sightseeing trip enjoyable? Place the following in order of importance:
   - a good guide or guide book
   - reading about the place before you go to see it
   - a good place to eat
   - good company
   - good weather
   - good souvenir shops

3. (weather) ....

....

PREVIEW

Who is Eddy talking to?
What do you think he
means by 'all this'?
What do you think the
'games' are?
Why is Eddy angry?

Please, tell me what this is all about. I don't like playing these games.

LANGUAGE USE

Interrogate	Then where did you go?
	What time did you leave the Barrier?
	Did you contact anyone?
	And you spent the evening at her house?
	Why didn't you ask Annie?
Ask for confirmation	You're the man in the lift, aren't you?
Talk about continuing events	Mr Judd and Mr Potter have been following you since yesterday.

WORDS AND EXPRESSIONS

check	file	after	Go on.
contact	game	nearby	Just a minute.
invite	job	since	This is (all) to do
meet	misunder-	yesterday	with ...
pick up	standing		
play	part		
report	reason		
	superior		
	tour		

VIEW AND ANSWER

1. Answer the questions.

1. Where is Judd standing?

(He's standing) By the door.

2. What is Archer looking at?

....

3. What does Archer show Eddy?

....

HOW WILL THEY SAY IT?

2. Study the following lines from the video. Decide how you think they will be spoken. For example, which word will receive the main stress? Will your voice go up or down at the end?

1. I told you. I went to the Thames Barrier.
2. What's all this about?
3. They have? Why?
4. You're the man in the lift, aren't you?
5. Wait a moment. I've answered all your questions, now you can answer mine.
6. Well, why didn't you ask Annie?

CHECK

3. Answer the questions.

1. How did Eddy and Maribel get to the Thames Barrier?

(They got there) By boat.

2. What time did they leave the Barrier?

....

....

3. How long have Judd and Potter been following Eddy?

....

....

4. Who is Miss Garcia?

....

5. Where did Eddy see Archer for the first time?

....

....

6. Where is Annie?

....

7. What does Archer ask Judd to do?

....

....

8. What does Eddy threaten to do?

....

....

9. Who is the head of security?

....

10. Why didn't Archer pick up Eddy before?

....

....

4. Tick the four statements which *best* describe Eddy's feelings.

1. He's relieved that he hasn't done anything wrong.

2. He's angry because Annie hasn't been able to go on her holiday.

3. He's pleased that Archer has managed to sort out the misunderstanding.

4. He can't understand why Archer didn't ask him these questions earlier.

5. He's angry that he has been followed for no reason at all.

6. He dislikes Archer.

7. He thinks Archer is the one who has stolen the keys.

EXPLAIN

– what Eddy means by 'for a reason' when he says: 'You think that my sister gave me those keys for a reason, don't you?'
– why Eddy is so angry with Archer.

VIEW AND LISTEN FOR DETAIL

5. Number the sentences in the correct order.

43.44

.... Yes, ... not really. I ... I picked them up off the desk. Just a minute ... You're the man in the lift, aren't you?

.... Yes, she did.

.... Did she give you these keys?

.... Correct.

.... No, no. Wait a moment. I've answered all your questions, now you can answer mine.

.... These keys ...

.... My sister works for you, doesn't she?

...**1**.... Did your sister offer you her flat for the weekend?

6. Complete the sentences with the missing verbs.

1. **42.45** Eddy: I ......_went_.......... to the Thames

   Barrier on the boat from the pier.

2. **43.07** Archer: Mr Judd and Mr Potter

   .... you since yesterday.

3. **43.29** Archer: And you ....

   the evening at her house?

4. **43.32** Eddy: Lisa and John...............................

   me to .... with them.

   I .... at a nearby guest house

   because I .... get into my

   sister's flat.

5. **44.22** Eddy: You think that my sister

   .... me those keys for a reason,

   .... you, before she

   .... on holiday? Well, you

   .... wrong. I

   .... up the wrong ones.

WORD STUDY

7. Circle the odd word in each group.

1. boat (house) river   water

2. contact   telephone   call   work

3. fetch   invite   offer   give

4. guest house   prison   bed and breakfast   hotel

5. head   superior   assistant   boss

8. The following words are often used as both a noun and a verb.

| call   contact   offer   telephone   work |

Complete the sentences, choosing from these words. Say whether they are used as a noun or a verb.

1. Did you ..._contact (v)_..... anyone?

2. I made a very useful ..._contact (n)_...... while I was there.

3. I won't take the job. It sounds like hard

   ....

4. Why don't you .... him? He's in the garden.

5. Would you .... Lisa some more tea?

6. Could you give me a .... tomorrow?

7. There's another .... in the bedroom, if you'd like to phone him.

8. She's going to .... for a computer company.

9. I'll .... him as soon as I get in.

10. She made me a very generous

    .... of the use of her car.

GRAMMAR PRACTICE

PRESENT PERFECT CONTINUOUS

How long have they been following us?

They have been following you { for three days.
since yesterday.

9. Using the notes below, make questions and answers about the characters. Use the present perfect continuous and, in the answers, a time expression with *for* or *since*.

1. Annie/wait in Archer's office/Saturday

How long has Annie been waiting in Archer's office?

Annie has been waiting in Archer's office since Saturday.

2. Judd and Potter/follow Eddy/a day

....
....
....
....

3. Eddy/study art and fashion/last year

....
....
....
....

4. Maribel/learn English/she was at school

....
....
....
....

5. Lisa/work as a telex operator/3 years

....
....
....
....

OPEN DIALOGUE

10. Mr Archer stops you on your way to school. Fill in your answers to his interrogation.

Archer: Just a few questions. Where are you going?

You: To school...

Archer: And that's where you are learning English?

You: ....

Archer: And how long have you been doing that?

You: ....

Archer: I see. Where have you just come from?

You: ....

Archer: Did you telephone anyone before you left?

You: ....

Archer: You're telling the truth, aren't you?

You: ....

Archer: OK. Now what did you do last night?

You: ....
....

Archer: Is that all? Didn't you do anything else?

You: ....
....

WRITE

11. Write a paragraph for the 'Student Profiles' page of a class magazine.

Say: your name, age and where you are from; what you do (if you have a job) and how long you've been working there; where you live and how long you've been living there; how many months or years you've been learning English.

DISCUSS

1. What do you think Mr Archer's home life is like? How does he spend a normal weekend?
2. Would you like to have Mr Archer as your superior? If not, why not?

PREVIEW

Whose passport has Archer got?
What is the holiday Archer is talking about?
Why has he rebooked it?

> Here's your passport, Miss Taylor. I've rebooked your holiday starting from today.

LANGUAGE USE

Talk about possession	Is this yours? Yes, it's mine.
Identify places	Which one is it? (It's) The one with the view of the sea.
Ask and talk about completed actions	I've rebooked your holiday. Have you had a chance to freshen up yet?
Make promises	I'll take care of your brother. You'll get them first thing in the morning.
Report requests	She asked me to telephone her.
Thank formally	Thank you for your help, Eddy.

WORDS AND EXPRESSIONS

apologise	inconvenience	Forget it.
clear up	property	in a fortnight's time
freshen up		That's fine.
rebook	tired	

VIEW AND ANSWER

I. Number these pictures in the correct order.

a)

Number ....

b)

Number ....

Number ....

c)

d)

Number ....

2. Write a sentence to describe what is happening in each picture.

1. Eddy is searching through his bag.

2. ....
   ....

3. ....
   ....

4. ....
   ....

CHECK

3. Answer the questions.

Who   1. apologises?

    Archer (apologises)...........................

    2. hug each other?

    ....

    ....

    3. is going to take Annie to the airport?

    ....

What   4. is missing from Annie's bag?

    ....

    5. is missing from Eddy's bag?

    ....

    6. did Maribel want Eddy to do?

    ....

    ....

Which   7. page of the brochure is the hotel on?

    ....

    8. hotel did Archer book for Annie?

    ....

When   9. is Eddy leaving London?

    ....

    ....

    10. will he get his videotapes back?

    ....

    ....

VIEW AND LISTEN FOR DETAIL

4. Complete the part of Mr Archer.

46.10

Archer: I 've booked a........... hotel for you. Page twelve. I hope you like it.

Annie: Which one is it?

Archer: .... view of the sea. The Majestic.

Annie: Yes, that's fine.

Archer: Good. Potter is waiting to take you to the airport. ....

.... freshen up yet?

Annie: No, I haven't.

Archer: Mr Judd will show you where.

5. What does Mr Archer say when he

1. **45.41** **gives permission** for Annie to leave?

You ..can leave........ now, Miss Taylor.

2. **46.06** **apologises** to Annie?

.... the inconvenience but you ....

3. **46.20** **describes** which hotel he has chosen?

The ....

....

4. **46.46** **asks** Judd to bring in the VCR?

.... the VCR please?

5. **46.58** **asks** about arrangements with Maribel?

....

.... with Miss Garcia?

6. **47.14** **promises** to return Eddy's tapes?

.... first thing in the morning

7. **47.23** **thanks** Eddy?

.... ,

Eddy. I hope you've enjoyed most of your weekend.

GRAMMAR PRACTICE

PRESENT PERFECT + *YET*

Have you had a chance to freshen up yet?

6. Make questions using the present perfect with yet and then answer them.

1. Annie/leave/for the airport?

Has Annie left for the airport yet?

No, she hasn't.

2. Eddy and Maribel/go/Thames Barrier?

....

....

....

3. John and Lisa/finish/decorating the house?

....

....

....

4. Eddy/send/any postcards?

....

....

....

5. Archer/see/Eddy's video?

....

....

....

6. Eddy/start/college project?

....

....

....

7. Maribel/see/herself on TV?

....

....

....

REPORTED REQUESTS

She asked me to telephone her.

7. Report what the people said using *asked ... to*.

1. **Archer:** (to Eddy) Please check your property.

Archer asked Eddy to check his property.

2. **Archer:** (to Annie) You can leave now, Miss Taylor.

....

....

3. **Archer:** Mr Judd will show you where (to freshen up).

....

....

....

4. **Archer:** Would you bring in the VCR please, Mr Judd?

....

....

5. **Maribel:** Could you phone me please, Eddy?

....

....

6. **Archer:** Mr Potter, would you drop Eddy on the way to Heathrow Airport?

....

....

....

WORD STUDY

8. Make an appropriate response to the sentences choosing from the list below.

Here you are.   That's OK.   Yes, of course.
It's mine.   Yes, I will.

1. Would you rebook my ticket?

Yes, of course.

2. Whose is this video camera?

....

3. Can I have my passport please?

....

4. Will you tell Annie I've gone home?

....

5. Thanks for all your help.

....

9. Look at the words below which are to do with crime. Notice how they are used. Rewrite the sentences using the verb suggested.

to **suspect** somebody **of doing** something
to **accuse** somebody **of doing** something
to **arrest** somebody **for doing** something
to **deny doing** something

1. I always thought Charles married Alexis for her money.

She always suspected Charles of

....

2. Mr Parks hid the razor blade in the loaf of bread and gave it to the prisoner.

The prison officer accused

....

....

3. **Man:** Madam, I saw you steal that bracelet just a moment ago. Please come with me.

He arrested

4. I tell you I have never seen this handbag!

She denied

....

ROLEPLAY

It is Sunday evening. You want to borrow something from your friend, eg cassette, dictionary, scarf or other item. You go round to your friend's house.

You	Your partner
Apologise for disturbing your friend.	Say you aren't busy.
Ask if your friend has had a nice weekend.	
	Reply.
Ask if you can borrow the item.	
	Ask which one.
Describe it.	
	Give permission.
Promise to return it first thing tomorrow.	
	Tell your friend where to leave it.
Confirm this and thank your friend.	

WRITE

10. Imagine that you have been watching this film on television. Write a letter to the television programme *What's your opinion?* saying what you think of the film *Two Days in Summer*.

DISCUSS

Do you think Archer was just doing his job?

THE STORY

1. Write questions for the answers below the pictures.

1. Why/go? Why did Eddy go to London?

To make a video for a college project.

2. Where/intend to stay? ....
....
At a guest house.

3. Where/meet Maribel? ....
....
In Covent Garden.

4. What/film? ....
.... The dress collection.

5. Where/go?
....
....
....
To Maribel and Lisa's house.

6. What/do? ....

....

They went sightseeing to the Thames Barrier.

8. Why/angry? ....

....

Because Archer had not asked the questions before.

9. How/apologise to Annie?

....

....

....

....

He rebooked her holiday in Greece.

7. How/start the conversation?

....

....

He asked them if they had enjoyed their day.

Write a summary of the story of *Two Days in Summer* in your notebook. Use the cues below and the pictures in exercise I as a guide.

Explain or describe

– who Eddy is and why he was coming to London.
– where he was going to stay and how he got the keys.
– how and where he met Maribel.

– his afternoon at the V and A.
– what happened when he got to Clapham.
– how he solved the problem.
– how he and Maribel spent the following morning.
– what happened on the boat trip back.
– why Eddy was so angry with Archer.
– what Archer did to apologise for the inconvenience he had caused.

GRAMMAR

3. Complete the conversation in a shop. Circle the right answer.

Maribel: Excuse me, how much are this/(these) T-shirts?

Assistant: The large one/ones are four pounds fifty. The others are all four pounds.

Maribel: OK. Can I have/take a large shirt/one, please. Oh, and I'd like/I like a present to/for my friend. Can I look for/look at those crystal ducks?

Assistant: Here you are/it is.

Maribel: Thank you. I have/'ll have the smaller size, please.

Assistant: Fine. How would you like/do you like to pay?

Maribel: Are you accepting/Do you accept credit cards?

Assistant: I'm afraid we don't/won't. But we do accept traveller's cheques.

Maribel: Good.

(Eddy approaches)

Eddy: Come on, Maribel. I am waiting/have been waiting for ages! The boat leaves soon.

Maribel: How long does the boat trip take/takes?

Eddy: About forty-five minutes. Did you bought/buy your presents?

Maribel: Yes, I did/bought.

Eddy: Look at that view of the Barrier! You brought your camera, don't/didn't you!

Maribel: Yes, let me take a picture of you, Eddy. Don't move. Smile.

Eddy: Hurry up!

Maribel: There! I give/I'll give you a copy if it's a nice one.

Eddy: Did you have/Have you had a chance of taking one of the Barrier yet?

Maribel: No. I would/am going to take one now. Isn't it a fantastic view!

CROSSWORD

Complete the crossword to find the hidden words.

1. Maribel bought her presents with a ... cheque. (10)
2. Eddy came to London for the ... (7)
3. Judd wondered if Maribel and Eddy had enjoyed their ... (6)
4. Archer asked Potter to ... Eddy on the way to the airport. (4)
5. What Annie wanted Archer to do. (9)
6. If today is Sunday, then ... was Saturday. (9)
7. You do this at night when you're tired. (5)
8. Archer apologised for causing this. (13)
9. Eddy's three video tapes take this number of hours to play. (4)
10. Eddy wanted to report Archer to his ... (8)
11. A method of transport. (11)
12. The whole business of the keys was just a ... (16)
13. The name of Annie's hotel. (8)
14. The hero of this film. (4)
15. Archer ... Annie's holiday. (8)

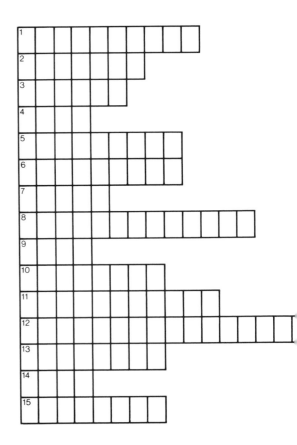

TWO DAYS IN SUMMER SUPERQUIZ

I. First, fill in each box on the chart below with the letter X, Y or Z. Don't show your partner what you are writing. Your partner does the same, so you each have a different chart.

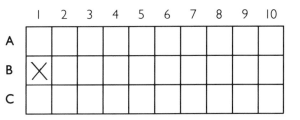

2. Choose a box and call it out to your partner, eg box 1B. If box 1B on your partner's chart has an X in it, your partner asks you any question from the list of X questions. Check the answer with your teacher if necessary. If you get it right, you write your score (1) in your box 1B on the chart below. If you get it wrong, you write 0 and go on to the next question.
X questions = 1 mark
Y questions = 2 marks
Z questions = 3 marks

	1	2	3	4	5	6	7	8	9	10
A										
B	1									
C										

3. Continue until you have each answered ten questions.

4. Add up your scores.

'X' questions (I mark)

1. In which part of London did Lisa and John live?
2. On which day of the week was the V and A closed?
3. Where was Eddy from?
4. Where did Maribel and Eddy go sightseeing?
5. Which sport didn't Potter like?
6. At what time did Eddy arrive at Kent House on Saturday morning?
7. What subject were Lisa and Maribel both studying?
8. What film was showing on TV on Saturday night?
9. In which department did Annie work?
10. What two types of sandwich did Judd buy for Potter?
11. What did Maribel buy for Lisa in the souvenir shop?
12. What was out of order in the V and A?

'Y' questions (2 marks)

1. Who wrote *Romeo and Juliet*?
2. Which famous pop group was John Lennon a member of?
3. What sort of things would you see at Madame Tussaud's?
4. Who lives at Number 10, Downing Street?
5. What famous couple married in St Paul's Cathedral on 29 July 1981?
6. What sort of things would you see in the National Gallery?
7. Which American president was involved in the Watergate Scandal?
8. What is the capital of Scotland?
9. What are the names of England's two oldest and most famous universities?
10. What food is Britain most famous for?
11. Who wrote *Oliver Twist*?
12. What is the capital of the USA?

'Z' questions (3 marks)

1. What are the names of Queen Elizabeth II's three sons?
2. What are the names of the two 'Houses' of Parliament?
3. Which countries are part of the United Kingdom?
4. What are the names of the three largest political parties in Britain?
5. What are the names of two national daily newspapers in Britain?
6. In which city did John Lennon die?
7. What are the names of London's two largest airports?
8. What does BBC stand for?
9. Which sport do you associate with the Grand National?
10. What is the name of the main shopping street in London?
11. Which country won the World Cup in 1986?
12. What does CIA stand for?

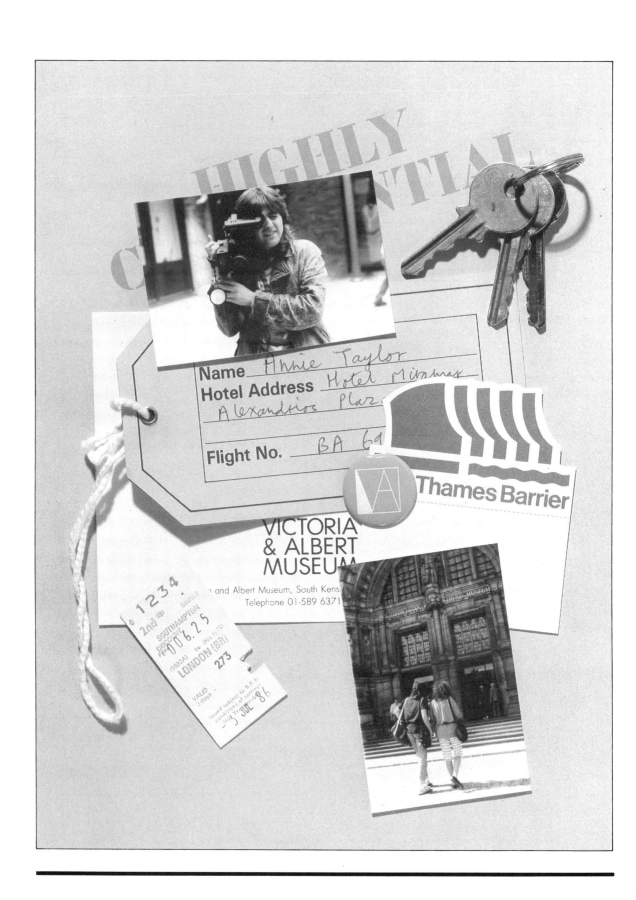

HIGHLY CONFIDENTIAL

Name Annie Taylor
Hotel Address Hotel Miramar
Alexandros Plaza

Flight No. BA 69

VICTORIA
& ALBERT
MUSEUM

and Albert Museum, South Kens.
Telephone 01-589 6371

Thames Barrier

0 1234
2nd
SINGLE
SOUTHAMPTON
006.25
(5982A) to (No 1175)
LONDON (BRI)
273
VALID
3 days
Issued subject to B.R.B.
conditions of carriage
3 30C 86